The heavens tell of the glory of God. Psalm 19:1

My Father's WORLD

Printed in Italy.
Concept by: Diane Stortz.
Project editor: Lindsay Black.
Art direction and design: Robert Glover.
Scripture quotations are taken from the Holy Bible, *New Living Translation*, copyright © 1996.
Used by permission of Tyndale House Publishers, Inc., Wheaton, Illinois 60189. All rights reserved.

ISBN 0-7847-1440-1

11 10 09 08 07 06 05 04   9 8 7 6 5 4 3 2 1

MUSIC TO SEE! ™

My Father's WORLD

illustrated by SELINA ALKO

STANDARD PUBLISHING
CINCINNATI, OHIO

This is my Father's world—

The heavens tell of the glory of God. Psalm 19:1

And to my listening ears,
all nature sings,

And round me rings
the music of the spheres.

All things bright and beautiful,

All creatures great and small,

This is my Father's world—

He made the things we can see
and the things we can't see. Colossians 1:16

I'm resting in the thought
of rocks and trees,
Of skies and seas—

His hands these wonders wrought.

All things bright and beautiful,

All creatures great and small,

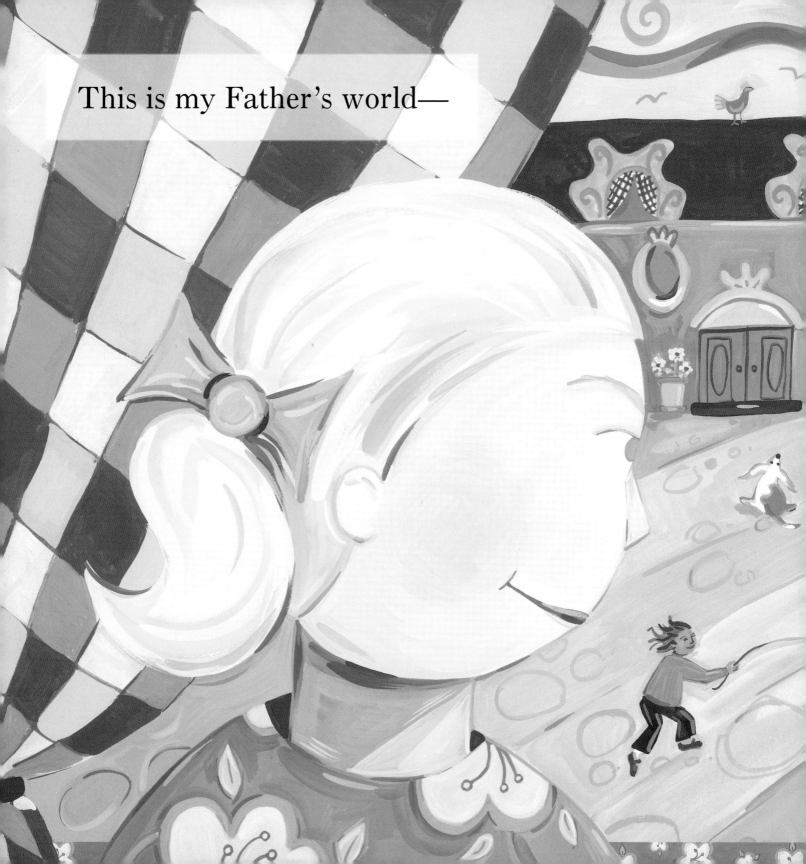

This is my Father's world—

God created people in his own image. Genesis 1:27

The birds their carols raise.
The morning light, the lily white
declare their maker's praise.

All things bright and beautiful,

All creatures great and small,

All things wise and wonderful,

The Lord God made them all.

This is my Father's world—

Everything God created is good. 1 Timothy 4:4

He shines in all that's fair.
In the rustling grass, I hear him pass—
He speaks to me everywhere.

All things bright and beautiful,

All creatures great and small,

All things wise and wonderful,

The Lord God made them all.

This is my Father's world—

Nothing exists that he didn't make. John 1:3

And may I not forget

That God is King;

let the heavens ring!

He reigns—let the earth be glad.

All Things Bright and Beautiful

Cecil Frances Alexander

This Is My Father's World